Small Creatures~

of the
Australian
Wilderness

Small Creatures~
of the Australian Wilderness

PHOTOGRAPHY LEO MEIER

TEXT DR A. J. PRESS

WATTLE BOOKS

A KEVIN WELDON PRODUCTION

ACKNOWLEDGEMENTS

The Publisher wishes to thank the following
individuals and organisations for their invaluable
assistance in the preparation of this book.

Director and Staff, Australian Museum, Sydney
Dariel Larkins R.A.O.U.
Associate Professor F.D.J. McDonald, University of Sydney
Mr G. Phipps, Macleay Museum
Dr R. Shine, Department of Zoology, University of Sydney

SPECIALIST EDITOR
J.R. Simons M.Sc.(Syd.), Ph.D.(Lond.)

TEXT
Dennis Hearne

PHOTOGRAPHY
Leo Meier

MANAGING EDITOR
Kerrie E. Andrews

PRODUCTION MANAGER
Cecille Weldon

DESIGN AND PRODUCTION
John Bull, Bull's Graphics

ILLUSTRATIONS AND FABRIC DESIGN
Isobelle Bruder

ADDITIONAL ILLUSTRATIONS
Yolande Bull

CAPTIONS FOR PHOTOGRAPHS PAGES 1-15

Page 1 An eastern water dragon *(Physignathus lesueurii)* from the Colo River region of New South Wales.

Pages 2-3 Mantids are close relatives of grasshoppers, crickets and phasmids.

Page 5 A tree frog from the Colo River region of New South Wales.

Pages 6-7 The misty world of the wilderness. A world of shadows and mystery. A world where even this majestic bird is dwarfed by the vastness.

Page 8 A damsel fly from Carnarvon Gorge, Western Australia.

Pages 10-11 An eastern grey kangaroo *(Macropus giganteus)* grazes peacefully in the foothills of the Victorian Alps.

Page 12 A sleepy moth, its wings and antennae glistening with early morning dew, rests on a flower stem … another day dawns in the Australian wilderness.

Pages 14-15 One of the smallest birds in Australia, the tiny *Cisticola,* balances delicately on a blade of grass.

A Kevin Weldon Production

First published 1984 by
Kevin Weldon and Associates Pty Ltd
43 Victoria St, McMahons Point, N.S.W. 2060, Australia
© Copyright Kevin Weldon 1984

National Library of Australia Cataloguing-in-Publication Data

Press, A. J. (Anthony James)
Small creatures of the Australian wilderness.

ISBN 0 949 708 062

1. Animals – Pictorial works.   2. Zoology – Australia –
Pictorial works.
I. Meier, Leo, 1951 – . II. Title.
591.994

Typeset by Walter Deblaere and Associates, Australia
Printed by Dai Nippon Printing Co. Ltd (Tokyo)

Foreword

*I*F ASKED to give an example of a beautiful animal, most of us, I guess, would think immediately of birds. Of all animals, they are the most conspicuous for their trim, stream-lined figures as well as their attractively coloured and patterned plumage. However, what about, for example, the corroboree frog or perhaps the lace monitor? They both sport attractively coloured and patterned coats. Most people, thinking no doubt about these kinds of animals, would probably hesitate to describe them in any stronger term than 'handsome'. I hope that the myriad superb photographs in this book, together with the information that accompanies them, will do much to alter this attitude. The true beauty of the creatures of the Australian wilderness can only be fully appreciated when they are seen in their environment and when their relationship to that environment is realised. The photographs, taken with considerable skill and art, wonderfully illustrate this. Here are mammals, birds and reptiles aplenty but there are also extensive treatments of the microworld of the lesser creatures – the lowly flat worm, primitive shellfish, spiders, insects and others. The conflict and competition of 'Nature red in tooth and claw' is perhaps more starkly seen in this world of leaf and twig, of forest litter and stream bank than it is in that of the more noticeable animals. Nevertheless, it is just as fascinatingly beautiful.

J. R. SIMONS M.Sc.(Syd.), Ph.D.(Lond)

Contents

FOREWORD   9

THIS VAST AUSTRALIA   17

DRIFT AND DIVERSITY   67

CREATURES GREAT AND SMALL   107
MAMMALS   107
BIRDS   113
AMPHIBIANS, REPTILES AND INVERTEBRATES   117

A MATTER OF LIFE OR DEATH   227

This Vast Australia

*I*T POURS in the Top End: warm, unrelenting rain that soaks through the ground. It pours in the south-west wilderness of Tasmania: cold, bitter rain that chills the vegetation. In the centre it bakes; in the Snowy it freezes. Scattered throughout this vast Australia, with all its different topography and climatic zones, are pockets of wilderness – natural zones man has left untouched for the small creatures of our insular continent to live much as they did two hundred years ago, before the first whites arrived and began widespread remoulding of the habitats they found.

About 40 000 years ago, humans first occupied the six million square kilometres that are Australia. They gradually had their effect on the country and, by the time of the modern Aborigines, with their practice of burning the countryside, great areas of grassland and open forest had developed. These areas, which looked promising for agriculture, were important in attracting European settlement. The subsequent development of agriculture and industry dramatically accelerated change in the face of the country and the lives of its creatures. Still, many creatures living in the remoter areas remain undisturbed. Despite the irregular rainfall, the arid interior is a haven to some. Others live high in the alpine regions where heavy snowfalls are more of a burden than man. Some species revel in the 4500 mm of monsoonal rain that swamps the Top End each year. Others are quite at home in the cold, wet Tasmanian wilderness.

*L*ittle wattlebirds *(Antochaera chrysoptera)* are honeyeaters that feed on grevilleas or any available nectar-laden flowers such as bottle-brushes. Despite being small, they will fiercely defend their territory in the shrubs and heathlands of the south-eastern Australian coast.

A dragon fly lies mummified, encrusted
with mineral salt on the bed of a hot water bore
in the Simpson Desert, a victim of the
harsh environment.

The diversity of habitats explains the wide range of fauna in the continent. Along the coast are sand dunes with stunted trees, tidal mud flats and mangroves which team with furiously scuttling crabs and molluscs which take life at a much more leisurely pace. Wading birds, ducks and the beautifully ponderous pelican live happily along the shoreline and in the freshwater pools and swamps behind the coastal dunes. The mangrove thickets, ugly and sinister to man, are a work of efficiency and beauty within the ecosystem. The oozing mud is rich with single-celled animals, bacteria and plants which break down the waste dropped by trees and their inhabitants or abandoned by the retreating tide. Birds, such as the mangrove warbler and mangrove honeyeater, and fish also make their home in this environment. One of the more curious inhabitants is the mudskipper, a fish which uses its fins as flippers to skip around the mudflats. Other fish use the mangrove estuaries as nurseries for, there, their young can thrive on the rich food supply.

The coastal wetlands are a sanctuary for thousands of birds. The great wetlands of the Top End team with birdlife. Beautiful magpie geese, whistling ducks and lotus birds flourish in huge numbers. The coastal swamps and rivers that do not dry up entirely in the dry season or in periods of drought are essential for the survival of the many waterfowl and, in this respect, the wetlands of Kakadu National Park are regarded as some of the most beautiful and important in the world. Before white settlement, littoral rainforests were scattered around the northern and eastern seaboards. Few remain today, although pockets have been preserved in the wilderness of Hinchinbrook and Kakadu. If they can be saved then so can the animals, such as the grey whistler bird of the Top End, that depend on them for food and safe breeding grounds. Inland from the coast, on the wind-battered hills, heathlands with their beautiful spring flowers on scrubby, stunted bushes, merge into tall open forests and woodlands. Many species, such as the giant rainforest snail and the southern angle-headed dragon, seek refuge in the dwindling patches of rainforest in gullies and valleys which have not been cleared by man.

Australia's sole major mountain chain, the Great Dividing Range, has an important effect on the continent's wildlife. It literally divides Australia, running from Cape York the entire length of the coast into Victoria. Along the Range, eucalypt woodlands and forests, interspersed with beautiful tropical and subtropical rainforests reach for the sunlight.

In Victoria and New South Wales' Barrington Tops and Lamington National Park, the remnants of once widespread, ancient rainforest dominated by Antarctic beech trees survive. In the highest and coldest areas, snowgum woodlands provide food and shelter.

On the western side of the Dividing Range, man has made an equally great impact on the original habitat. The forests once surrendered to woodlands and savannah but these areas proved ideal for sheep farming and wheat. Farmers razed vast areas of vegetation and, with it, many of the small creatures who had lived there. The plains once held a wide variety of habitats – scrub, woodlands, mulga and brigalow – but gradually primary producers have cleared the land. Some species may have vanished, while others, such as the bilby, numbat and bridled nail-tailed wallaby, lost vast areas of their original range. The wallaby once lived in an area from the Murray River to above Rockhampton and was a common sight to early explorers. It now exists in only one small pocket of 11 000 ha west of Rockhampton.

The magnificent Simpson Desert is another such refuge. The Simpson stretches from south-western Queensland into the Northern Territory and northern South Australia. Rolling sand hills are broken by gibber plains and it is only this harsher environment, with its unpredictable rainfall, high daytime temperatures and food shortages, in which many species are now found. Some, such as the small insectivorous marsupials, live deep down in the dry cracks of the plains, emerging in the cool of night to feed. Others, such as the shield shrimp, found their own 'aquatic way of life' in a desert where water is a rare resource. Frogs, too, make the desert home.

Like many other creatures of the Australian wilderness, adult male dragon flies occupy and defend a territory. The dragon fly mating procedure is quite complex: the male grasps the female behind the head by a pair of claspers at the end of his abdomen. The pair may then fly about together for some time, then settle and, by flexing their abdomens, the tip of the female abdomen comes into contact with the male genital area just behind the thorax.

Australia is an island continent
surrounded by coastline that, from the dune
habitat through to the mangroves and coastal
wetlands, supports vast numbers of small creatures.
The coastal habitat pictured occurs on
Hinchinbrook Island, North Queensland.

(over)

Much of inland Australia, such as
the Simpson Desert, pictured, is semi-arid to arid
and relies on only intermittent rain to support life.
In the baked claypans, stony deserts and sandy
deserts, small creatures have adapted to survive
without water, sometimes for many years.

A dry leaf or a piece of bark is a quite
acceptable nesting place for Lesueur's frog *(Litoria
lesueurii)*, for this terrestrial frog is often found
long distances from water. The species grows
to only about 7 cm long.

The masterpiece of one of the weaver ants – in this case a green tree ant *(Oecophylla species)* – is a collection of leaves drawn together by ants forming chain gangs with their bodies and then sewn together by silken thread produced by the ant pupa. Each pupa is handled and applied to the leaves by a worker ant, somewhat in the manner of using a 'glue pot'.

A red-tailed black cockatoo
(Calyptorhynchus magnificus) looks down
haughtily from its tree perch in Kakadu National
Park, Northern Territory. The birds can grow up
to 62 cm and nest in any tree with a suitable
hollow. In the north, these cockatoos are
common and gather in large flocks.

In its favourite habitat of open forest,
a white-plumed honeyeater *(Lichenostomus
penicillatus)* rests on a branch. One of the
best-known Australian honeyeaters, it feeds
on nectar and insects – for which its slender,
recurved beak is adapted – over a large
area of the continent.

LOTUS BIRD

The extraordinarily long toes of the
lotus bird or lily trotter *(Irediparra gallinacea)*
enable it to walk easily across surface-floating
aquatic vegetation, thus earning it the irreverent
nickname of Christbird. Despite the lack of
webbed feet, it swims well and dives underwater
when threatened, thus swimming to safety. It can
also change the colour of its rooster-like comb
from red to yellow if alarmed. Lotus birds feed
mainly on aquatic plants and insects, probing
the mud and vegetation as they step nimbly
across their water plant 'pontoons'. Found in
northern and north-eastern Australia, they
are often observed, stretched out on
their sides, sunbathing.

Lotus bird of Kakadu National Park, Northern Territory.

In mating, the male spider's objective
is to approach the female and quickly transplant
a packet of sperm without arousing her
antagonism. In order to encourage success,
a male species of *Dinopus* makes a kind of
'flag' of thread and waves it as he approaches
the female. Most spiders have a special sequence
of signals and responses in the mating ritual.

A swamp wallaby (*Wallabia bicolor*)
stands alert and watchful. Swamp wallabies are
common from the brigalow belt of Queensland
through to south-western Victoria. Once believed
to have been common also in South Australia
in times past, it is most likely that sightings
made early this century in south-eastern
South Australia were 'strays' from across
the Victorian border.

Pelicans *(Pelecanus conspicillatus)*
breed in all parts of Australia where there are
lakes and swamps, as well as by the sea. Noted
for their clumsy take-off, they are nevertheless
efficient flyers and can soar to 3000 m
in thermal currents.

S and monitor *(Varanus gouldii)* in the
Simpson Desert foraging for food in a temporary
pool of water. Sand monitors are lizards which
grow to 1.6 m and occur throughout most of
Australia except the extreme south-east and the
wettest parts of the east coast.

Skinks form the largest group of Australian lizards. Their legs are noticeably small compared with their bodies and, in some species, legs are completely absent. Skink species vary, from the small common garden lizard to the large blue-tongues; many are viviparous. Here, two demonstrate the lizard method of mating.

Poisonous cane toads *(Bufo marinus)*
were introduced from Hawaii in 1935 to protect
sugar cane crops from cane beetle. They multiplied
out of hand and are now a major pest in
Queensland where they breed in still or
slow-moving water.

SATIN BOWER BIRD

Males of the satin bower bird species
(Ptilonorhynchus violaceus) dance, display their
plumage and fan their tails to attract a mate to
their decorated bowers during the breeding
season. Bowers are made of twigs and sticks
woven into two walls which the male blackens
with charcoal. Alongside the corridor-like bower
is built a platform for the display of decorations
– fruit, seeds, feathers, flowers and, in recent
times, even pieces of plastic – mostly coloured
blue. At sunrise when all is ready, the male begins
displaying the decorations in its beak, making
whirring noises, fanning its tail and dancing
around the display ground. Once a female has
been thus successfully enticed, the pair mate
in the bower itself. During autumn and winter,
satin bower birds form semi-nomadic flocks but,
in spring, return to the same mating territory
where males renovate their old bowers or build
new ones with twigs from the former bower.

lowers are often constructed to attract pollinating insects and many small flower spiders live in or near blossoms. In nature's way, these spiders are often coloured and patterned to resemble the preferred flower of residence.

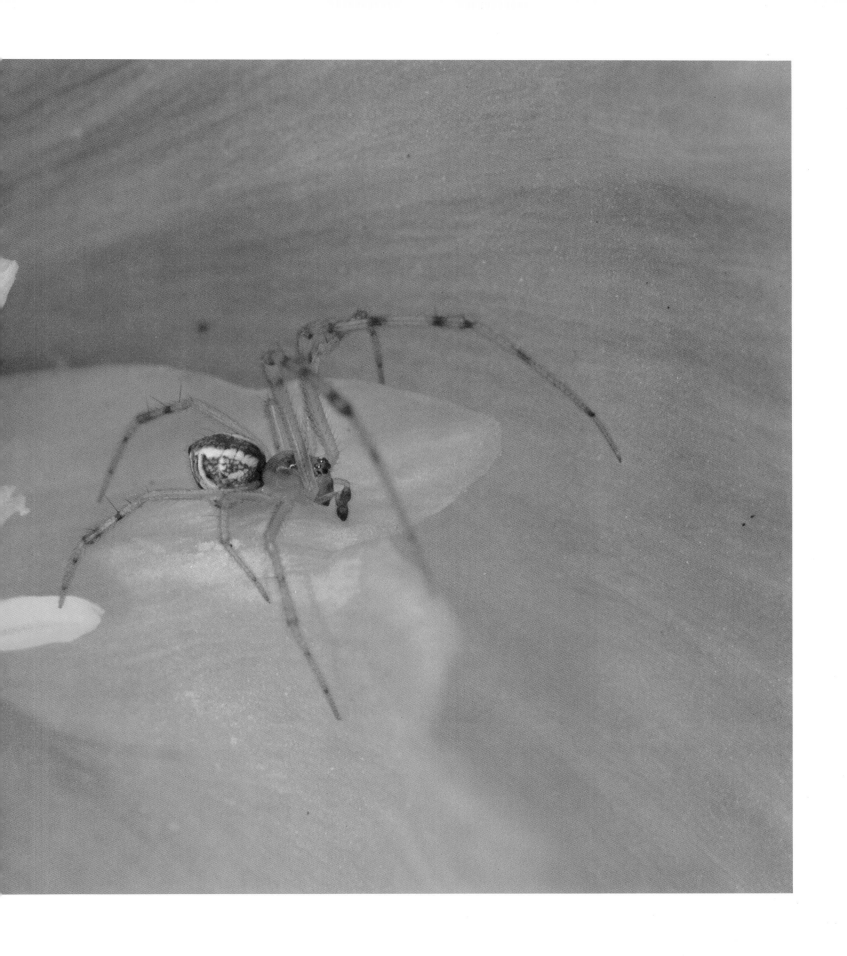

Australia has many tree-dwelling
ants which live in hollow twigs and other cavities.
Here, one of the larger species is dragging
a fly back to its nest after fending off the
spider in whose web the prey was snared.

The large egret *(Egretta alba)* is a graceful
bird with a neck longer than its body. Found in
lakes, swamps, estuaries, dams and mangroves,
it feeds on insects, crustaceans, fish
and amphibians.

A koala *(Phascolarctos cinereus),* lolling up
in a tree as usual. Koalas sleep during the day
and feed at night on the leaves of just a few species
of eucalyptus, poisonous to most animals but
safe for koalas which are equipped with livers
capable of detoxifying the food.

SHORT-BEAKED ECHIDNA

Like its relative, the platypus, the short-beaked echidna *(Tachyglossus aculeatus)* is a monotreme: despite being a mammal, it lays eggs and does not have nipples. The Australian short-beaked echidna and its close cousin, the long-beaked echidna of New Guinea, lack teeth. Echidnas feed on ants and termites by digging up nests or mounds with their powerful claws and poking long, sticky tongues into the cracks and crevices. When frightened or attacked, echidnas curl up into tight balls, using their long spines for defence. The short-beaked echidna is relatively common, being found throughout Australia from the coast to the desert.

Crested pigeons *(Ocyphaps lophotes)*
have come to terms with European settlement:
while at home in the wilderness, they are also
content to live on farms and around homesteads.
Here the distinctive crest stands highlighted
by the outback sky.

The larval caterpillar stage of this moth clearly shows the sideways cutting jaws and the method in which they are used to bite into a leaf.

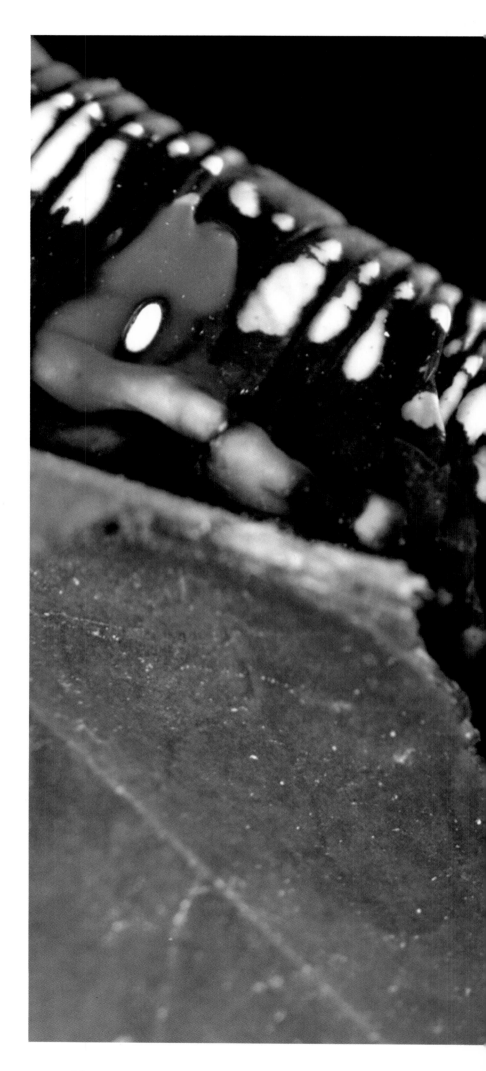

An ornate dragon *(Amphibolurus ornatus)*
was sighted in the Fitzgerald River region of
Western Australia. All lizards in the group are
egg-layers, producing clutches ranging from
two to three in the smallest species up to nearly
thirty in the case of the bearded dragon.

Diamond doves *(Geopelia cuneata)* roost
in trees but feed on the ground and break into
a strange wobble when they run. In flight,
they are fast and direct, with a pronounced
swooping flight pattern on long journeys.

FAT-TAILED DUNNART

Many of Australia's mouse-sized marsupial mammals are rarely seen and the fat-tailed dunnart *(Sminthopsis crassicaudata)* is a classic example. A shy creature which feeds by night and hides in cracks in the mud, under logs or in grass tussocks during the day, it earns its odd name from the fat stored in its tail as an energy reserve for lean times when its natural food of insects and other invertebrates runs low. Despite being rarely seen, the fat-tailed dunnart ranges over much of Central Australia as well as south-western Queensland, New South Wales, Victoria and Western Australia.

Most spiders weave some type
of web to trap their prey, sometimes an untidy
tangle of threads but, with orb-weaving spiders
(in this case *Eriphora* species), it is a beautifully
constructed spiral of thread stretched out
over radial supports.

Peron's tree frog *(Litoria peronii)* is a common tree frog of eastern Australia, often found on branches and trunks of trees, especially paperbarks, in wet environments.

Drift and Diversity

D IVERSITY of habitats provides for a diversity of species unique enough in the world to inspire the imaginations of early theorists. One theory held that the animals came 'island hopping' through Asia and the Malay Archipelago, across Indonesia and New Guinea and ultimately journeying down Cape York. This may still be true of some of the 'new Australians' such as the native rats, bats and the eastern water dragon. However, it is likely that much of Australia's fauna has less in common with the fauna of Asia than was once thought.

Most scientists, supported by evidence in geology, zoology, botany and palaeontology, now believe Australia was once part of a super continent: Gondwanaland. We shared this giant land mass with South America, Africa, India, Anarctica, New Guinea and New Zealand. More than 160 million years ago, the Great Southern Continent began breaking up. First to split away was Africa (about 160 million years ago). India followed 125 million years ago and began to drift towards Asia. New Zealand is believed to have gone its own way about 80 million years ago when Australia and New Guinea were still connected to South America.

As recently as 55 million years ago, Australia broke away and moved rapidly north. Australia still moves north as the rate of several centimetres a year and each year the evidence in favour of the continental drift theory gains new strength. For example, Peter Barrett, a New Zealand geologist,

L ike a puppet from a children's fantasy
play, the eastern water dragon *(Physignathus
lesueurii)* poses obligingly. A semi-aquatic arboreal
lizard, it is quite often seen on tree branches
overhanging creeks and rivers.

Spider web threads are made of protein
and represent a considerable investment on the
part of the spider. If the web is destroyed, the spider
may not have sufficient reserves to make another
and so starves to death; to dismantle a web,
the spider will eat it and thus conserve protein.
The fly, pictured, was entrapped by four of the
sticky spiral threads. The fine radial threads are
not sticky and therefore are left undisturbed.

found in 1968 the fossil of an extinct amphibian 600 km from the South Pole. The discovery held enormous significance since the fossil, more than 200 million years old, had also been found in southern Africa and India. Other fossils of ancient mammal-like reptiles have been found linking the fauna of South America, India, Antarctica, Australia and Africa. In 1982, the presence of fossil amphibians and other terrestrial animals in Antarctica suggested that this great icy wilderness must have been much closer to the equator and that it had a much more benign climate.

As the land masses separated, the species began adapting slowly to their newly created environments. The better adapted a species, the better its chances of survival and so the characteristics which most help a species to survive will be perpetuated in breeding. One possible example in Australia of natural selection in progress is the wingless grasshopper *(Keyaris scurra)*, found on the southern tablelands and slopes of New South Wales. Two races of the grasshopper have emerged, each with a different number of chromosomes. One 'tribe' lives on the tablelands; the other on the slopes. Occasionally they interbreed but the hybrids are less successful at reproducing than either of the two pure 'tribes'! Gradually the two races are growing apart, each presumably coping better with their respective environments.

The family of long-horned grasshoppers
(Tettigoniidae) have typically long feelers.
The long-horned grasshopper, pictured,
is a female; her ovipositor extends tail-like behind
her body as she clings to a reed in the Daintree
River region of far North Queensland.

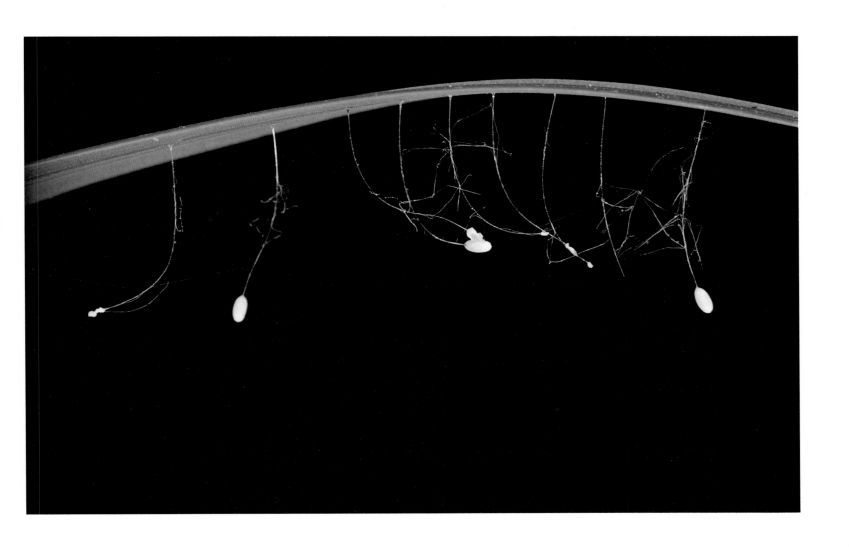

Eggs of one of the lacewings *(Neuroptera*
species). Some lacewings, after the larvae hatch,
are ant lions and in these cases the eggs are
laid in sand so the larvae can trap ants in
their little sandpits.

One of the delightfully pretty aquatic
molluscs, the nudibranch *(Hypselodoris bennetti),*
produces a less colourful brown egg-spiral.
Nudibranches are unusual molluscs in that they
have lost their shells altogether and are so
named because the gills are exposed – here seen
as a purple tuft at the animal's rear. The
pink 'horns' are tentacles, its highly
developed sensory organs.

A mollusc grows its shell as a result
of a secretion from the 'mantle' membrane.
The mantle is usually hidden under the shell but,
in some cases, it extends outwards and envelops
the shell, as in the bubble shell *(Hydatina physis)*,
pictured, and cowries.

FRESHWATER CRAYFISH

More than a hundred species of freshwater
crayfish are unique to Australia and range from
the Tasmanian *Astracopsis gouldi,* a giant which
tips the scales at 3.5 kg and is up to 40 cm long,
through to the Queensland *Tenuibranchiuris
glypticus,* a featherweight at just a few grammes
and less than 2.5 cm in length. Some species live
entirely in water; others make their homes in
bogs and marshy swamps. In dry periods, crayfish
burrow deep into riverbanks or natural dams or
hide under damp vegetation to avoid drying out.
The *Euastacus sulcatus,* pictured, was found
in Washpool, northern New South Wales.

Bull ants *(Mymecia* species) are primitive ants and extremely aggressive with a ferocious sting. Usually, only a few dozen inhabit a nest.

True flies have only one pair of wings;
all other insects have two pairs. The second pair of
wings in flies is reduced to small, knob-like
appendages which vibrate and act as gyroscopes
for stable flight.

Lygaeid bugs are small creatures that
live near water and inhabit rushes and sedges like
those that occur on Hinchinbrook Island,
Queensland, where this one was photographed.

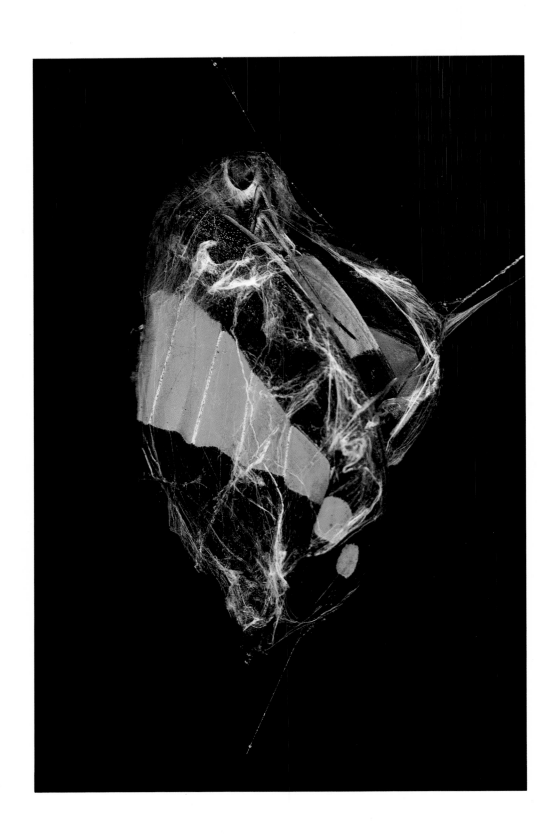

A spider has caught a hapless blue
triangle butterfly and wound threads around its
victim to secure it firmly. Often in this state
the victim is paralysed by the spider's venom and
'stored' for a later feast.

Insects fall into two major groups —
those that undergo complete change from egg to
larva to pupa then adult stage and those that
undergo only slight change between the newly
hatched, or nymph, and adult stages. Mosquitoes
belong to the first category: after the egg and
larval stage, the adults emerge from and rest
on their pupal cases to dry their wings.

The gaudily plumed rainbow lorikeet *(Trichoglossus haematodus)* shows why it is a favourite with photographers and painters. Frequent in most timbered areas, where it feeds noisily and greedily on nectar-laden blossoms, its habitat extends to the offshore islands of Queensland.

Cicadas

It is fifty years since the great explorer and
naturalist, H. H. Finlayson, wrote of the cicadas
in Central Australia: 'Here, in the fierce
sunlight... the males begin their terrific song
... the noise was tremendous and all pervading.
When it ceased for a moment the relief was like
the lifting of a burden. It went on day and night
for a week or more...'. Most Australians are
familiar with the shrill 'shriek' of the cicada,
a sound created by the insect rapidly vibrating
a tightly stretched membrane covering a
drum-like structure on its abdomen. Cicadas
feed by piercing the bark of trees and shrubs
with their 'beaks' and sucking the sap as it
dribbles out. They also lay eggs in the bark;
when the nymphs hatch they drop to the ground
and bury themselves, feeding on the sap of the
roots. They remain underground for up to two
years, emerging to burst out of their shells
and sing for their lifetime – a few short weeks.

Cicadas of central Queensland in various stages of emergence from their pupal shells.

A white-breasted sea eagle *(Haliaeetus leucogaster)* sits proudly on a desolate tree. Sea eagles live on a wide diet of fish, sea snakes, ducks, rabbits and carrion.

Coreid bugs, like many other bugs,
are generally brightly coloured in order to warn
predators that they are distasteful – if not
poisonous. As a further deterrent they can exude
a fluid which is repugnant both in smell and
taste. In the photograph, two adult coreids
mate on a thistle head.

Spiders are notable as creatures of prey but not all set snares to capture their victims. Huntsman spiders, for example actively pursue insects in order to obtain food.

The extremely common larvae of the
large grey hawk moth *(Psilogramma menephron)*
occurs nearly everywhere in Australia, even urban
gardens in hedges and thickets of vegetation.

One of the gaudiest of butterflies,
rarely subdued in colouring, is the Jezebel
butterfly, sometimes called a 'painted lady'.

(over)

The aristocratic, southern angle-headed
dragon *(Gonocephalus spinipes)* observed here in the
Lamington National Park of Queensland, is a
rainforest dweller. Its numbers are thought to be
declining owing to rainforest logging programmes.

BATS

Australia's sixty species of bats fall into
two main groups: the fruit bats (Megachiroptera)
and the insectivorous bats (Microchiroptera).
The insect-eaters are generally small, some
with a wingspan of 30 cm and a weight of 200 g,
but most are much smaller. Fruit bats, on the
other hand, can grow quite large, weighing more
than 1 kg and with a wingspan of up to 150 cm.
Fruit bats roost during the daytime, often in
groups of thousands. Many insectivorous bats
hunt their prey by 'echo location' – emitting
a short, rapid, high-pitched sound which bounces
back off a flying insect and allows the bat
to home in on its prey. The lesser long-eared
bat *(Nyctophilus geoffroyi),* pictured, is of
the insectivorous bat group.

While they do not make webs, hunting spiders such as jumping spiders *(Opsthoncus* species) can still produce thread as a 'safety line' when they jump or climb. As an indication of its courage, this particular jumping spider has vanquished a wasp, a common predator of spiders.

Ants, like their relatives the bees
and wasps, are usually social insects constructing
their nests to contain from a few dozen to many
thousands of individuals. Many ants, but
not all, dwell underground.

The eastern yellow robin (*Eopsaltria australis*) freezes – a common defence against intruders – but, in search of food, it is lightning fast as it darts after ants and bugs. Eastern yellow robins stay together in family units often for up to six months at a time.

KING CRICKETS

Of the many species of crickets occurring
throughout Australia, the largest, the king
crickets, are unique to this country. They grow
up to 12 cm long, a formidable sight with large
mandibles and powerful forelimbs to grasp their
prey. The many species of king crickets are
found throughout the country, from rainforests
to deserts; in the arid inland they live in
burrows excavated from the inhospitable ground.
The species living an easier life in temperate
habitats hide in tree holes, bogs or under leaves
during the day and emerge at night to feed
on small insects. Some species turn
cannibal when food is scarce.

Creatures Great and Small

*F*OR THE past 55 million years, Australia has been virtually isolated, allowing for its animal population to diversify along its own unique lines. The mammal population is particularly interesting since the Australian region is the only one with representatives of all three remaining orders of mammals – the monotremes, marsupials and placentals. Yet Australia is not only a land of kangaroos and egg-laying mammals, for it also has some fascinating creatures amongst the rest of the animal kingdom, including birds, amphibians, reptiles and the invertebrates.

MAMMALS

MONOTREMES

Australia's platypus, that weird and wonderful creature of schoolbooks, films, even cartoons, is one of only three monotremes in the world. Two of them occur only in Australia: beside the platypus there is the short-beaked echidna. The long-beaked echidna is found only in New Guinea. These unusual creatures not only lay eggs. They also suckle their young on milk from glands on the chest and belly rather than via nipples. Monotremes are the oldest group of mammals – survivors of an ancient era. They appear to be solely Australian in origin and may have evolved as the continent separated from Gondwanaland. Their reptilian characteristic of laying eggs indicates their ancestry but does not explain how the monotremes evolved to have so many unusual characteristics.

*T*he tree frog *Litoria latopalmata,*
photographed in the Daintree River region of far
North Queensland, is often found hunting on the
forest floor far from water. Like most frogs it is
nocturnal and it is similar in many other respects to
its southern relative, Freycinet's frog *(Litoria freycineti).*

Preparing for a dash to safety,
a red-necked pademelon *(Thylogale thetis)*
in the Lamington National Park of Queensland
is poised on its hind legs. When moving leisurely,
it ambles along on all fours, dragging its
non-supportive tail behind. Red-necked
pademelons live mainly in rainforests and dense
eucalypt forests, coming into the open to feed.

The platypus is also Australia's only truly aquatic mammal. While the echidna is purely terrestrial, the platypus took to water but can also travel overland quite freely when it moves between waterholes. Because the platypus closes its eyes, nose and ears when it swims underwater, it uses its soft and extremely sensitive bill as its guide to nuzzle around in the silt and gravel of streams in search of the invertebrates upon which it feeds. When the platypus nests and raises its young, it builds a burrow in the bank of a river or stream in keeping with its aquatic lifestyle.

MARSUPIALS

The platypus has aroused curiosity around the world but it is the kangaroo that has become Australia's 'trademark'. Kangaroos, though, are only a part of the more than 120 species of Australian marsupials – those curious, pouched creatures, with their young in pockets, that stunned the first white explorers.

All marsupials give birth to young often only millimetres long. Instinctively, they crawl through their mother's fur to the safety of her nipple, usually in an enclosed pouch. There they develop from blind, hairless embryos into juvenile marsupials. Marsupials were so labelled, from the Latin word for pouch, because the first of their kind that were described by early zoologists did, indeed, have pouches and, although many of our best known marsupials do have pouches, such as kangaroos and wallabies, some do not. The small marsupial mice, amongst others, carry their young attached to their nipples underneath them, an amazing feat of survival when it is considered that a 30 g mother can carry eight babies weighing 10 g each.

Fossil evidence suggests that the marsupials once spread over more of the world than just Australia. A recent discovery in Antarctica suggests the marsupials once roamed there; they are believed to have originated in North America and spread to South America when it was still united with Australia. It was after Australia split from Antarctica and began its lone drift through the ocean, however, that our marsupials began their great transformation into so many different forms.

The oldest marsupials are probably the dasyurids which are carnivorous and which bear some resemblance to the opossums of South America. They range from the tiny desert-dwelling planigales, weighing

R abbits *(Oryctolagus cuniculus)* were
introduced to Australia in 1858 and have now
spread over most of the continent, destroying
much of the native grassland – both directly by
feeding and indirectly by baring the soil and
digging burrows. In association with white man's
early unwise agricultural methods, rabbits have
been responsible for massive soil erosion
and resulting habitat destruction for
many native fauna.

only a few grammes, to the large Tasmanian tiger and the probably extinct thylacine. The carnivorous marsupials are fierce hunters, the largest of them even hunting small wallabies, reptiles and possums.

The best known group of marsupials in Australia includes kangaroos, wombats, possums and the endearing koala, all scientifically known as the diprotodons. All evolved to be herbivorous with two cutting teeth in front and grinding teeth at the back. They have adapted to occupy most habitats in Australia, although with differing lifestyles. Some, such as the wombats, kangaroos and wallabies, are terrestrial grazers. Others, like possums and koalas, are arboreal – tree dwelling – and eat leaves. Further evolution within the possums themselves has given some of them a flap of skin between the front and hind legs which allows them to glide between trees for greater mobility on their nocturnal forays.

The bandicoots are a mixture of both types of marsupials. Omnivorous – eating insects as well as roots and fruits – bandicoots are like the carnivorous marsupials in that they have many teeth but, like the herbivores, their second and third toes on the hindfoot are joined. Once there were eleven species of bandicoot in Australia but, sadly, four are probably now extinct, owing either directly or indirectly to man's incursions into their range.

As the carnivorous mammals were evolving, so was a strange little character called the marsupial mole *(Notoryctes typhlops)*. Superficially similar to the moles of Europe, Asia and America, it spends most of its life underground, is blind and has ears that are merely holes surrounded by dense fur. However, the marsupial mole is not placental like the true moles. From a mysterious ancestry the marsupial mole has, for no apparent reason, developed an appearance and lifestyle similar to a totally unrelated mammal tens of thousands of miles away.

PLACENTAL MAMMALS

Apart from dingoes, two land-based placental mammal groups occur in Australia – rodents and bats. In comparison with the marsupials and the monotremes they are newcomers but, despite their late start, they have spread throughout the continent. Rodents first reached here through New Guinea about fifteen million years ago. The water rat has adopted a semi-aquatic lifestyle, eating freshwater insects and crustaceans.

Like a spectator at a tennis match,
a little pied cormorant *(Phalacrocorax melanoleucos)*
stares intently to one side. More common
on inland waterways than the coast, little pied
cormorants have adapted to underwater fishing
yet swim by the unusual manner of paddling
both feet simultaneously.

Others, such as the hopping mice of inland Australia, have developed long back legs. While most native rats and mice are terrestrial, some, such as the tree rat, are able to forage and nest in trees.

The bats that occur in Australia consist of some sixty species in two major groups – the fruit bats and the insectivorous bats. Fruit bats, with wing spans up to a metre across, are a common sight around many cities and towns. The insect eaters are generally much smaller, most weighing less than 200 g, and live in forests and caves throughout the country.

Other placental mammals are marine species, such as seals, whales and dugongs, and occur in the coastal waters of Australia. Dugongs, or 'sea cows', are the only herbivorous marine mammals. Australian waters north of the Tropic of Capricorn house the largest population in the world. Unfortunately, the great dugongs make excellent eating and, despite being protected, they are suffering from over-exploitation as well as being drowned in fishing nets.

BIRDS

Australia has more than seven hundred species of birds, including probably our most recognisable species, the emu. Fossil evidence reveals that an emu at least 2 m tall was present seven million years ago. It is even possible this giant may have survived as recently as the time of the Aboriginal migration about 40 000 years ago. Of all the Australian birds, only twenty-three have been introduced deliberately since white settlement; a few others have recently reached Australia under their own 'steam' and have successfully colonised the continent. The cattle egret, for example, was first recorded in the Northern Territory in the 1900s but seemed to have vanished until, in 1948, flocks of hundreds descended in waves on Arnhem land. Now the cattle egret occurs through all the coastal belts and ranges. Similarly, the sarus crane, now found in patches of the Northern Territory and the Gulf Country, was not recorded before 1966 when a sighting was made in north-western Queensland.

Australia is rich with other species – hawks and eagles, kingfishers (including kookaburras), pigeons, ground-dwelling birds, weavers, native finches, many seabirds and varied waterfowl among them. Our parrots and honeyeaters are particularly interesting. Parrots are made up of more

than fifty species, falling mainly into the following groups: cockatoos, lorikeets, fig parrots, broad-tailed parrots, long-tailed parrots and typical parrots. The largest are the cockatoos, ranging in size from the palm cockatoo (from Cape York Pennisula) to galahs and corellas. Cockatoos have large, powerful beaks for crushing seeds and some, like the yellow-tailed and white-tailed cockatoos, use their beaks to tear bark off trees and dig out the larvae of wood-boring insects which form a large part of their diet. Some have even more specialised diets. The glossy black cockatoo found in eastern Australia feeds almost exclusively on the seeds of the native she-oak.

Among the prettiest of our small parrots are the lorikeets. Their tongues, highly specialised to assist them in their feeding, develop into a 'brush' at the tip in order to extract nectar from flowers. The lorikeets live almost entirely on sweets!

Another parrot group with an esoteric diet is composed of the fig parrots. The double-eyed fig parrot *(Psittaculirostris diopthalma)* earns its odd name from the spots, near each eye, which give the appearance of two eyes joined together when viewed from the front. In isolated communities in northern New South Wales and coastal Queensland, the double-eyed fig parrot lives almost exclusively on the fruits of native fig trees but, like many other birds, the seeds and fruits of other plants and even insects can be digested in times of food shortage.

Pretty as they are, lorikeets do not have spectacular colours to themselves. The rosellas and other broad-tailed parrots also provide flashes of bright colour as they hurtle through the trees. Their beautiful deep reds and blues, the vivid yellow and greens and the more subtle turquoise and pinks make them the target of bird fanciers who will pay a small fortune for their illegal exportation to countries around the world. Some of our rosellas, such as the crimson and the eastern, are relatively common, but others, such as the night parrot, which live in the arid and semi-arid regions may be extinct. There have been no recent sightings of the night parrot and if it is still alive it is in extremely isolated corners of the Simpson Desert.

Some of the sixty-six species of honeyeaters in Australia face the same crisis as the parrots. The white-lined honeyeater, for instance, now lives only in the vast wilderness of the Top End. As their name suggests, honeyeaters live primarily on a diet of nectar although some do feed

A magnificent study on the edge
of a broken limb, the blue-winged kookaburra
(Dacelo leachii) is the closest relative of the
common laughing kookaburra. Like its cousin,
it defends its territory, circling an intruder
and 'barking' raucously.

A lone bird has the sunset to itself —
the vast wilderness of our island continent left
to a solitary sentry.

extensively on insects. They have adapted to their diet by developing curved and narrow beaks which probe into blossoms. Within the beaks are long, brush-tipped tongues which honeyeaters can also roll to suck up the nectar. Generally, the honeyeaters have rich and interesting calls but some, such as the wattle bird and the friar bird, are loud and raucous. Perhaps it is in defiance of the odd picture nature painted of them. The wattlebird has coloured flaps of skin, or 'wattles', hanging down from the sides of its head. The friar bird is stranger still, with a bare forehead and a flap of dark skin on its crown.

REPTILES, AMPHIBIANS AND INVERTEBRATES

They creep, they crawl, they slither, they slip in and out of dark, mysterious waters. The reptiles, amphibians, and creepy-crawlies of Australia are some of our least-loved creatures but they hold a fascination all their own.

AMPHIBIANS

Amphibians – frogs, toads, newts and similar – spend at least one stage of their life in the water. Of the 2500 species of frogs in the world, about 150 are found in Australia, even in the arid interior where little or irregular water supplies are found. The water-holding frog is a prime example of an amphibian which has adapted to a life where water is often the most uncommon resource. The cane toad was introduced into Queensland in the 1930s to control the cane beetle and must now rank as part of our fauna. It has gained a deserved notoriety. By 1980 its numbers had spread from the sugar cane fields of Queensland down to northern New South Wales as well as up into Cape York and across the Gulf Country. Not only do cane toads prey on small native animals but they are poisonous to most predators; even snakes have been found dead with partly-digested toads inside them.

REPTILES

Amphibians probably evolved 250 million years ago before the disintegration of Gondwanaland. Reptiles, in turn, evolved from amphibians and enjoyed their greatest strength about 120 million years ago

Common in eastern Australia is the
lace monitor *(Varanus varius)* which climbs
trees in search of birds' eggs and nestlings.
Lace monitors can lash out with their tails
as weapons but, more usually, tend to display
discretion rather than valour.

when flying versions ruled the air and huge terrestrial ones stomped the land. In modern times, only four main groups of reptiles have survived throughout the world: crocodiles and alligators, turtles (sometimes called tortoises), snakes and lizards and, last, the ancient tuataras of New Zealand. Two species of crocodile, the saltwater and the freshwater, occur in the coastal regions of northern and north-eastern Australia. We have twenty-two species of turtle, some saltwater, others aquatic or semi-aquatic in the major river systems and streams. However, the most successful reptiles in Australia are the snakes and lizards. They are spread throughout the continent, on the coast, in the ranges and in the desert.

The largest of the lizards is the perenty *(Varanus giganteus),* which grows to about 2.5 m. The smallest and some of the most beautiful are the geckoes and skinks. Lizards are primarily carnivorous, feeding on insects, small vertebrates such as frogs and mice and, less often, on vegetable matter. The larger lizards such as the monitors (also known popularly as goannas) are voracious predators. Some lizards display a variety of colours for camouflage; others choose bright colours or, as in the case of the bearded dragon, use menaces to frighten their enemies. One group of lizards has a superficial similarity to snakes. These burrowing species have, over time, had so little use for their legs that, gradually, successive generations have shed all or most of their limbs. One lizard family, the legless lizards, are unique to Australia and New Guinea and, like snakes, have elongated bodies to suit their burrowing lifestyle.

About 110 species of snakes exist in Australia. Twenty-eight of these are potentially dangerous to man: the taipan, king brown, death adder, tiger snake and copperhead are in fact among the deadliest in the world. The rest of our snakes are not only harmless – they are quite beautiful. Snakes range throughout Australia in a variety of habitats. Some, such as the Arafura file snake, live in the water but most are terrestrial. One group of terrestrial snakes are burrowers, which includes the virtually eyeless, blind snake. Still others, such as the green tree snake *(Dendrelaphis punctulatus),* are arboreal and spend most of their time in trees hunting for prey.

INVERTEBRATES

When the unique and beautiful fauna of Australia is discussed, the humble invertebrates – insects, spiders, snails, crustaceans and many more – are often overlooked. One of the difficulties in assessing the origins and affili-

Molluscs occur in two forms – univalves
and bivalves (double-shelled). Univalves, with
a single shell or no shell, include snails, periwinkles,
octopi and squid. Most are aquatic but many snails,
such as the land snail *(Thersites novaehollandiae),*
have adapted to terrestrial life by using the
mantle cavity – which houses the gland from which
the shell is produced – as a lung. Their tongues
resemble a miniature file by which they rasp
away fragments of their preferred food.

ations of Australia's invertebrate fauna is the lack of fossil records, unlike the fossil evidence for mammals and birds whose bones are often well preserved. Despite this, the invertebrates outnumber all the vertebrates many times over. Not only are they small but they are so abundant in the bush that they are regarded often as pests. Nevertheless, our continent does have many unique invertebrates, some quite beautiful, others so ancient that they have changed little over the past two hundred million years. The mountain shrimp *(Anaspides tasmaniae)* for example, belongs to an ancient order of animals known as syncarids. Once known only as fossils, living examples have been found recently in mainland Australia, Africa, Asia and Europe. Mountain shrimps feed on algae, detritus and smaller animals. In Australia they occur in the highlands of Tasmania and are reasonably common in the south-western Tasmanian wilderness in streams and pools.

A bearded dragon *(Amphibolorus barbatus)* suns itself in a 'dug-out'. Bearded dragons are often seen sunbaking on country roads and roadside fenceposts.

Galahs *(Cacatua roseicapilla)* have a
surprisingly high 'infant mortality' rate, despite
the large flocks familiar to most Australians.
Only ten per cent of fledglings survive to become
adults; as a compensation, they then
live for many years.

MOUNTAIN BRUSHTAIL POSSUM

The mountain brushtail possum or bobuck
(Trichosurus caninus) is a close relative of the
common possum which often lives in cities and
towns. The mountain brushtail, however, prefers
eucalypt forests and rainforests from southern
Queensland to Victoria and is a stickler for
territory, marking out its domain with the scent
glands on its chin, chest and anus. Mountain
brushtails are mainly nocturnal feeders, primarily
ranging through trees but also sometimes on
the ground in their search for leaves, fruit
and fungi. During the day they sleep it off in
the safety of old tree hollows or logs.

The most widely distributed of all
Australian lizards is *Cryptobletharus boutonii.*
This tree lizard also occurs on other continents and
islands of the world where, in dry areas, it is found
under the bark of trees. It often descends to the
ground to feed on small insects.

Peering out menacingly from its
rockside home is a children's python *(Liasis
childreni)* a nocturnal snake, mainly terrestrial
but with the ability to take to trees. It feeds on
small mammals, birds and reptiles. The children's
python was named after its discoverer, not because
it is a playmate for the young.

Hover flies frequently lay their eggs on various bugs and aphids, on which the parasitic larvae feed before pupating.

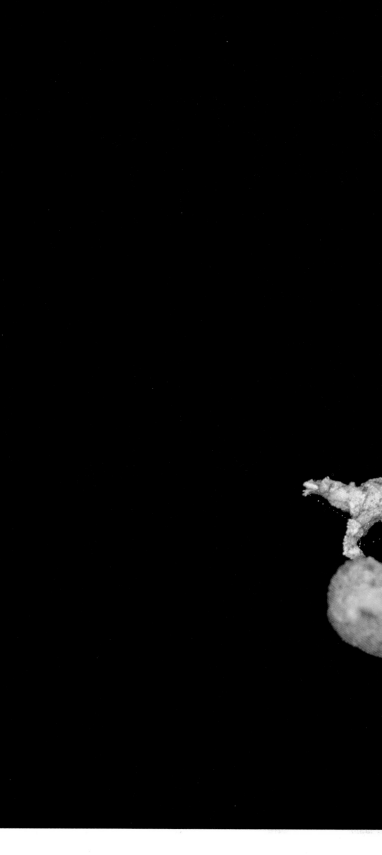

Pied stilts are more at home in swamps
and marshlands but were here photographed flying
over the Simpson Desert after heavy rain.

A pied stilt *(Himantopus himantopus),*
in search of plants and small animals, wades in water
after the monsoonal rains in Kakadu National
Park, Northern Territory.

BEARDED DRAGON

Despite its strong jaws, the bearded dragon
(Amphibolurus barbatus) has little defence against
predators, Rather, it relies on fear tactics –
flaring its 'beard', in reality a flap of skin, and
exposing its bright yellow mouth to discourage
attackers. The bearded dragon is a reptile
and eats worms, insects, small mammals and
lizards. Commonly seen basking on rocks or
tree stumps, it is found in most habitats
of eastern Australia.

With neck and head outstretched,
the darter *(Anhinga melanogaster)* gives a
perfect demonstration of why it is also
called the snake bird.

Plumed whistling ducks *(Dendrocygna eytoni)*
and water whistling ducks *(Dendrocygna arcuata)*
mingle happily on the marshes of Kakadu National
Park in the Northern Territory. Whistling ducks
earn their name from the shrill sound made
both by their wings and voice boxes.

Like all Australian freshwater turtles,
the head of *Chelodina rugosa* cannot be pulled
straight back into the protective shell. Rather, it is
laid sideways. One Aboriginal legend has it that the
turtle came about when a snake totem hero,
surrounded by enemies, fastened two shields to
his body, one to protect his front and
the other his back.

Slugs are common in moist habitats
and help in breaking down organic matter.
They evolved from snail-like molluscs and the
species illustrated still shows traces of its
ancestors' shell position.

SUPERB BLUE WREN

In the breeding season, from September to
February, males of the superb blue wren species
(Malurus cyaneus) display the coloured plumage
for which they have become justly famous.
The female, however, is a drab grey-brown tone.
The brilliant blue and black markings on the
head and neck of the male make it easily identi-
fiable in its habitat of south-eastern Australia
and up into the highlands. Superb blue wrens
live in thick, low vegetation in extended family
groups consisting of a number of adult males and
their entourages – they breed in rapid succession,
enabling them to raise many young. Their
territories are less than one hectare in
area and these they defend vigorously
against intruding wrens.

Superb blue wren of the Colo River region, New South Wales.

Common in temperate rainforest,
dry woodland and, where these birds were
photographed, in alpine woodland, yellow black-
tailed cockatoos *(Calyptorhynchus funereus)*
nest in safe tree hollows high above the ground.

ommon seagulls are the garbage
collectors and waste disposers of beaches, bays,
parks and rubbish dumps and thrive in the presence
of man. More elegantly known as silver gulls
(Larus novaehollandiae), they are occasionally
found inland, along lake and river edges.

The generally 'hairy', feather-like
antennae common to moths are evident in the
lymantrid moth. Actually, the 'hairs' are
large, downy scales.

Royal spoonbills *(Platalea regia)* fly in
tight formation, like a well-disciplined air force
squadron, constantly nomadic in search of water
where they may sweep their spoon-like bills
through the water to strain out their preferred
food of small fish and crustaceans.

Royal spoonbills in flight.

The six-spined spider *(Gastercantha minax)*
is of the orb-weaving type and is often referred to
as one of the bird-drop spiders because of the
camouflage pattern and colours.

A dragon fly *(Telephlebia* species)
newly emerged from its nymph stage. The young
nymphs resemble the adults except that the
nymphs do not have wings; as the adults emerge
they must dry their wings, here by standing
on the nymphal shell after having crawled
up a reed blade from the aquatic world
in which the nymphs live.

WATERHOLDING FROG

The waterholding frog *(Cyclorana platycephalus)*
is an amphibian superbly adapted for the arid
regions of Australia. The frogs live in the Centre's
temporary pools and lakes but, when the water
inevitably dries up, they bury themselves
deep in the mud, shedding part of their skin to
form a cocoon. They live happily on their
reserves of fat and water, sitting motionless for
up to five years or until the next substantial rain,
when they emerge to feed and breed. The eggs
are spawned and stick to vegetation or sink
into the mud, taking from fourteen to forty days
to develop from eggs to tadpoles to little frogs.
The Aborigines of Central Australia knew of
these frogs and searched for them in dried-up
ponds when in need of an emergency water supply.

A jumping spider slowly creeps up
on its prey and then pounces on it. Jumping spiders
have well developed eyesight and forwardly placed
eyes to aid in their search for food.

A white ibis *(Threskiornis molucca)* stands
majestically on a tree, surveying the surroundings.
In flight, flocks of ibis hold a 'V' formation,
all flapping their wings or gliding in unison.
They feed on frogs, fish, crustaceans and
snails and break water molluscs open with
their strong bills.

Caterpillars, the larvae of moths and
butterflies, are variously adapted for survival.
Perhaps the most common adaptation amongst
the many species is the presence of
thousands of urticating hairs that deter
both man and beast.

Grasshoppers are closely related to
crickets and, like them, are equipped with strong
jaws which bite sideways to demolish even
tough plant material with ease.

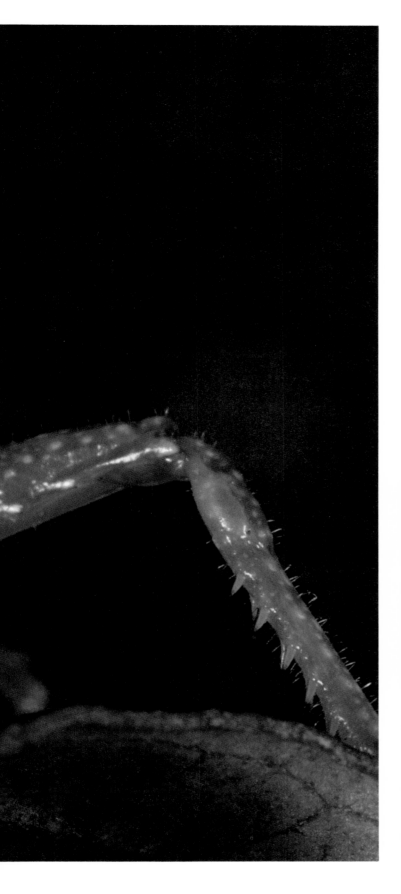

Grasshoppers, as well as the closely related crickets, have well-adapted jaws for chewing their favourite food – the leaves of trees and shrubs.

Generally hiding by day, processional
caterpillars emerge at night to follow the leader
to a suitable location to feed or pupate. They
eventully emerge as moths, the females of which
are easily recognisable by the dense tuft of
'hairs' around the end of the abdomen.

MOUNTAIN GRASSHOPPER

High in the alpine regions lives one of
Australia's most beautiful grasshoppers – and
one of the most unusual. The male and female
mountain grasshoppers *(Acripeza reticulata)* are
vastly different. The male has true wings and
looks like the garden variety grasshopper familiar
to most urban Australians. Its mate, however,
lacks the wings and looks more like a weevil.
The two sexes share a beautiful colouration –
bright blue and red bands, interspersed
with black, which they reveal as a threat
device when alarmed.

The only Australian stork, the jabiru
(Xenorhynchus asiaticus), occurs mainly along the
northern and north-eastern Australian coasts but
has been known to wander further south. The
glossy, distinctively shaped head of the jabiru
has also earned it the name of 'policeman bird'.
Note the extremely long legs adapted for wading.

Ichneumon wasps parasitise a wide variety
of insects and spiders. The host can be paralysed
by the female wasp's sting and the eggs are then
laid on or into its body. Sometimes the hatched
wasp larvae consume the living host; in other
cases the larval wasp does not hatch until the
host itself pupates, at which stage the host
is consumed and the pupal case used by the wasp
to develop to adulthood.

High in the Victorian Alps, a shy
eastern yellow robin peers curiously at intruders.
Eastern yellow robins keep a close watch on
visitors straying too close to their nests
during the breeding season.

A flock of wading knots *(Calidris canutis)* on Hinchinbrook Island in Queensland. They frequent beaches and mudflats and are unusual in that they submerge both beak and head in the ooze in search of food.

Dragon flies catch their prey in flight,
hence have excellent vision and powers of flight.
Like the helicopter, they are aerodynamically
designed. Dragon flies are often imagined to
be stinging insects but they are, in fact, harmless.

HUNTSMEN SPIDERS

The poor huntsmen have often been mislabelled 'triantalope' and/or 'tarantula' – those deadly spiders of the northern hemisphere to which the huntsmen bear a superficial resemblance. The huntsmen occur in almost all habitats and, while their bite can be nasty, they are not deadly. Their flattened bodies and long legs enable them to scuttle into cracks or under tree bark where a spider would seem unable to fit. Huntsmen seek their prey by night, scuttling sideways as well as forwards in a distinctive style before pouncing on their victims. While one of the more popular beliefs about spiders is that the female is aggressive to the male, often eating him during mating, huntsmen seem to be particularly loving – one has been recorded mating for up to ten hours! Pictured is the huntsman *Isopoda* species.

Moths are expert at camouflage and
display not only greatly varied colouration but also,
in some cases, quite bizarre body shapes to blend
in with their environment.

Geometrid moths, like hawk moths,
are excellent flyers. The wings are aerodynamically
shaped to resemble a miniature hang-glider.

Magpie geese or pied geese *(Anseranas semipalmata)* are now rarely found more than eighty kilometres from the coast and mainly in the north, as here, stared at by water buffalo in Kakadu National Park. However, in former times, they would wander over the entire continent, especially in the dry season.

Mantids, which are close relatives of grasshoppers, crickets and phasmids, have the first pair of legs lined with spines and developed for grappling. Once caught in their grasp, nothing escapes.

Although ground dwelling, sand
monitors are quite versatile: they can climb trees or,
alternatively, form a 'tripod' with hind legs and
tail in order to gain extra height for surveying
the scene. The sand monitor pictured scampered
to safety up a tree in the Fitzgerald River
region of Western Australia.

Brown falcons, also called browns hawks
(Falco berigora), do not chase prey in flight.
They prefer to sit quietly on a high perch, studying
the ground in search of small mammals and
reptiles upon which they will swoop, using
their strong talons for the kill.

TREE FROGS

The drab green frog of children's books
is a far cry from the beauty of the spotted thigh
frog *(Litoria cyclorhynchus),* below, and the
green and golden bell frog *(Litoria aurea),* left.
Many species of tree frogs are found in Australia,
ranging in size from 2 cm to a mammoth 150 cm.
In general, they have large discs on their fingers
and toes which help in climbing. However,
not all tree frogs actually live in trees; some are
completely terrestrial. The spotted thigh frog,
below, from the Fitzgerald River area of
south-western Australia, is one of only three
species of *Litoria* found in that area.

Tree frog from the Washpool rainforest behind Grafton, New South Wales.

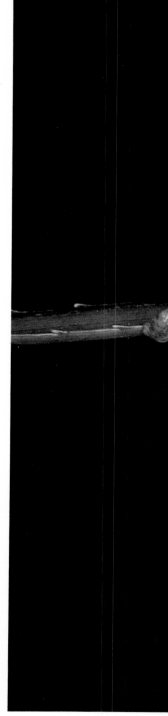

Tree frogs occur in most parts of Australia and were
photographed in the Fitzgerald River region of Western
Australia (top left), and in the Colo River region of
New South Wales (bottom left and above).

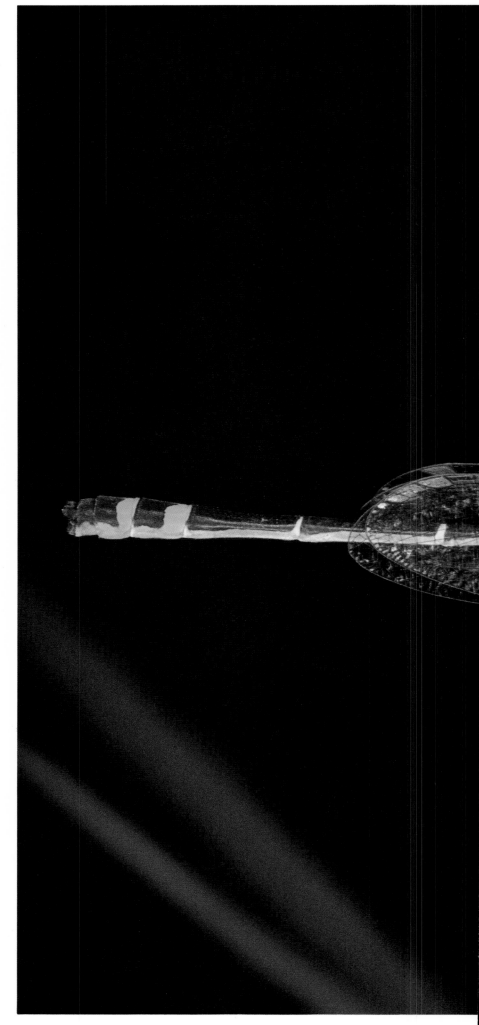

Damsel flies (*Austrochnemuis* species) differ from dragon flies in their smaller, more delicate appearance as well as various zoological features of their wings and mouths. Both damsel and dragon flies are members of one of the most ancient lines of insects, known from Carboniferous times which ended some 270 million years ago. They are always found near fresh water.

According to Aboriginal legend,
the laughing kookaburra's famous cry was a signal
for the sky people to send out the sun.
The truth is less flamboyant for the call
of the laughing kookaburra *(Dacelo novaeguineae)*
is actually to advise intruders of the boundaries
of its family's territory.

In usually rowdy flocks of up to several
thousand, little corellas *(Cacatua sanguinea)* are
often found dominating a tree in central Australia.
When they breed, however, they become silent
and secretive. Little corellas prefer eating
the seeds of native grasses rather than
cultivated grain crops.

Mites are related to ticks and
spiders and, like them, feed on the juices of some
living organism. Red spider mites are no exception
and attack with gusto many exotic garden
and crop plants.

The pretty eurymelids occur mainly
in Australia, living in association with ants from
whom they receive a sugary 'milk'. Some species
actually live in ants' nests.

Like a miniature cicada, to which they
are distantly related, the cicadellids, pictured,
and eurymelids feed on the juices of flowering
plants. These bugs, like others, are sap-sucking.

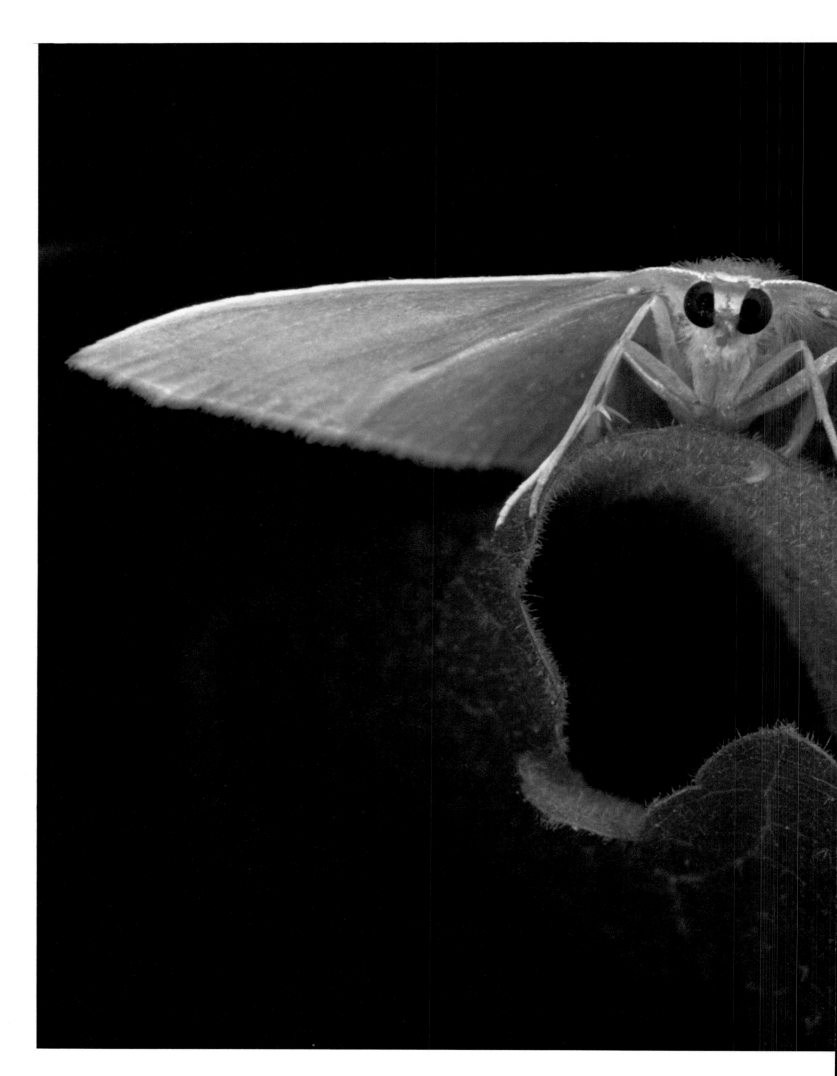

Geometrid moths, like hawk moths, are excellent flyers. The wings are aerodynamically shaped to resemble a miniature hang-glider.

Geometrid moths *(Thalaina* species)
are so called because their larval stage – caterpillars
– move with a looping motion as though measuring
out a stretch of branch or leaf. Such contortionist
feats also enable them to resemble twigs as they
rest on their preferred food source of wattle trees.

Arafura File Snake

Called the file snake after its rough scales,
the Arafura file snake *(Acrochordus arafurae)* is
totally aquatic, swimming rapidly and gracefully
and feeding exclusively on fish it hunts
underwater. File snakes have loose skin that,
out of the water, looks three sizes too big but,
when the snake begins swimming, the skin
flattens out and acts as a type of paddle. Like
many Australian snakes, file snakes give birth
to live young rather than laying immature eggs.
Arafura file snakes are placid animals; they are
neither poisonous nor do they bite. Originally
called the Javan file snake, the Australian reptile
was recently named as a distinct species and took
its new scientific and common names from the
Arafura Sea – it occurs mainly in the rivers and
wetlands of the Northern Territory, Gulf of
Carpentaria and Cape York Peninsula.

Scarab beetles include the common
Christmas beetle *(Anoplognathus olivieri).*
The fat, white larvae have brown-tinged heads and
mouth parts and are quite curved in appearance.
They feed underground on roots and organic
matter. Adults are adorned with a strong
iridescent colouring.

The larvae of cup moth *(Doratifera* species)
have rosettes of stinging hairs which are erect when
the caterpillar is disturbed and are used to
discourage predators. In many species, hairs also
festoon the pupal case to protect the dormant
creature as it **metamorphoses** into its adult form

W eavils are actually beetles with
the head region in the form of a long snout that
enables them to pierce and extract the flesh
from grains and seeds. The jewel weavil
(Chrysalopus spectablis) was one of the first
insects collected in Australia by Sir Joseph Banks
in 1788. The larvae feed on the trunks and
branches of wattle trees.

Bugs are all sucking insects, having
mouth parts that can form a tube to pierce the
surface of plant leaves and stems and suck up
the juices. Like cicadas and leaf hoppers, the
young resemble the adults except for being
wingless in the nymph stage, as the developing
nymph coreid bug illustrates.

Jewel insects, including the buprestid
beetles (*Stigmodera* species and others), gained their
common name from both their pretty colouring
and relatively small size. As adults, they are
usually found around flowers but the larvae
are most often borers of trunks, roots and leaves.

The powerful, exposed jaws of one
of the carabid beetles *(Calasoma schayeri)* make
short work of its food – the caterpillars of
butterflies and moths.

Hinchinbrook Island's soft green setting seems a perfect home for the peaceful dove *(Geopelia striata)*. Often seen in pairs or small groups, peaceful doves gather in flocks near water or at a favourite feeding place.

Phasmids are stick insects that live
on plant foliage and are close relatives of
grasshoppers and crickets. Masters of camouflage
and capable of staying immobile for hours,
they have evolved to resemble the twigs
of their environment.

Hawk moths *(Celerio* species), as the
name implies, are fast and strong flyers that can
often hover, like a hummingbird, in front of flowers
to extract nectar with their protruding mouth
parts. Note the long and narrow front wings, rather
like a delta jet plane, and shorter rear wings
for power in flight.

Leaf beetles are known as chrysomelids
and are generally small and brightly coloured.
The hundreds of species, in both the larval and
adult stages, feed on foliage and can cause
massive destruction of crops.

A handsome black and white skink of the Australian rainforests, *Carlia vivax* displays a red spot behind each eye.

ZEBRA FINCH

The zebra finch *(Poephila guttata)* was the water
beacon for the Aborigines and first white
explorers of Central Australia. The seed-eating
zebra finch must drink water at least once a day
and, preferably, every hour, so that those that
live in the relatively dry interior usually
inhabit areas where there is some permanent
water. Zebra finches cannot always be trusted,
however, since they are also able to suck
up dew from leaves during severe water
shortages. Although widespread over most
of Australia, zebra finches congregate mainly
in the interior, often in flocks of up to a hundred.
Like many other Australian creatures that rely
on irregular rainfalls, they are opportunistic
breeders, having their young after a rainy
spell regardless of the season.

A female wolf spider *(Geolycosa* species)
with her babies which she carries about with her
until they can fend for themselves. Wolf spiders
do not spin a web; rather, as the name suggests,
they run their prey down to make a kill.

The creature that has fallen victim
to the ant is peripatus *(Peripatus* species) an odd
animal that represents the evolutionary link
between the worm-like organisms and those with
jointed limbs, such as insects, crustaceans and
so on. With many anatomical features resembling
those of earth worms, peripatus nevertheless
has insect-like antennae, respiratory system
and muscular, clawed legs.

Fine scales provide the 'velvety' feel of
the velvet geckoes which occur nowhere else but
Australia. The reticulated velvet gecko *(Oedura
reticulata)* and its relatives have pads on toes
and fingers to enable them to cling to smooth
surfaces, even if completely upside down.

Scavengers of the north, fork-tailed kites
(Milvus migrans) are often seen around slaughter-
houses, stock yards and rubbish dumps. They also
congregate where there is a plague of rodents
or grasshoppers, thriving on the easy pickings.

A stern-looking, blotched blue-tongue
lizard *(Tiliqua nigrolutea)* was observed in the
Victorian Alps where, unlike its relative, the
common blue-tongue, it is quite active at low
temperatures. Blotched blue-tongues are also
found in Tasmania and the islands of Bass Strait.

The Australian crow butterfly *(Euploea core),*
is often seen in flocks. The larva feeds on fig trees
in places such as Kakadu National Park. The pupae
are initially pink but then become attractively
patterned in pink and gold, thus appearing,
like Christmas decorations on the chosen
tree of residence.

Many wasps lay their eggs on caterpillars which provide a ready-made meal for the wasp larvae when they hatch. Having consumed and thereby killed the caterpillars, the wasps pupate in little white cocoons.

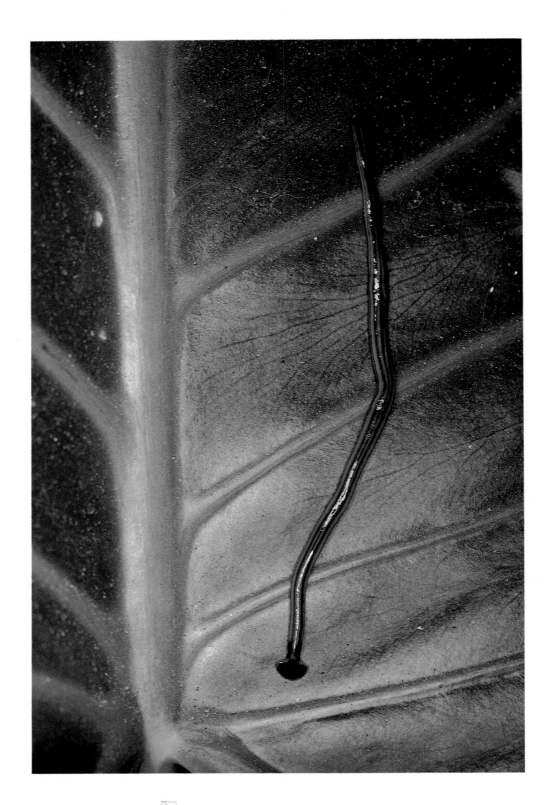

Flat worms (planarians) are amongst
the lowliest of terrestrial creatures. They need
a moist environment and glide over surfaces by
means of millions of tiny, hair-like structures that,
like minute oars, move in a rowing action.
The *Bipalium* species pictured is unusual
in that, unlike most flatworms, it spends most
of its life away from the ground on trees and shrubs.

The snail, pictured, became the scorched
victim of bushfire in Kakadu National Park,
Northern Territory.

A Matter of Life or Death

*T*HE SMALL creatures of the wilderness are safe as long as there is a wilderness. Sadly, though, many species are being added to a growing list of endangered fauna. Ten to twenty million years ago Australia had a giant marsupial era. A wombat the size of a hippo and a kangaroo standing more than 3 m tall roamed the plains. We even had a carnivore resembling a lion – the marsupial thylacoleo. The only trace of their existence remains in fossil records; nature overtook them. In modern times it is man, not nature, who is overtaking species by changing the environment too quickly for them to adapt. One species becoming extinct can threaten a second and so on in a chain reaction – the entire nature of an ecosystem can change dramatically with the disappearance or addition of just one species. The removal of a predator can allow its prey to multiply until they can grow out of hand, devouring food supplies and in turn threatening the existence of another group by starving them to death.

Possily one per cent, or about thirty-six species, of mammals have become extinct in the world in the past 350 years. A further 120 are so rare they are in danger of extinction. Ninety-four species of birds have vanished in the same term; a further 187 are threatened. With man has come his cohorts – the cats and dogs who turn feral, for example, and prove more successful in the wild than the original inhabitants. In Australia, the

*R*egent bowerbirds *(Sericulus chrysocephalus)*
live mainly in the upper levels of forest trees,
coming to the ground only for bower-making,
mating and display dancing. Regents occur in
rainforests from Mackay on the Queensland
central coast to the Hawkesbury
River near Sydney.

A juvenile black falcon *(Falco subniger)*.
The birds prey on native quail, swooping down
and catching them up with their extremely
powerful talons. It is most unusual for these
high-flying, high-roosting birds to be
seen on the ground.

eastern quoll (native cat) was no match for the feral cats and dogs who competed for its food. Rivalry and disease have led to an abrupt decline in the numbers of the eastern quoll, to such an extent that it may now be extinct over most of its former range. Sheep, cattle, horses, goats and rabbits have changed the grazing patterns through vast tracts of Australia and, in turn, killed off or endangered many species of herbivores.

Up to sixteen mammals are believed extinct in Australia. Twenty mammal species that once roamed the area of New South Wales no longer do and a further five species in New South Wales are on 'death row'. New South Wales, with its intensive development in comparison with much of Australia, is worth individual study in the light of endangered species. The yellow-footed rock wallaby, the bridled nail-tailed wallaby, mountain pygmy possum, eastern quoll and white-footed marsupial mouse have suffered from habitat destruction and competition from introduced animals. Birds are often safer because of their mobility, yet forty-two species in New South Wales are at risk because of habitat changes. Lord Howe Island, the tiny satellite of the State, is the last refuge of four bird species, including the Lord Howe Island woodhen.

Nationally, the patterns of New South Wales are being repeated. The approachable and slow flying Burdekin duck, for instance, once a common sight from the Richmond River in New South Wales through to the Top End and to the Fitzroy in Western Australia, has now disappeared from New South Wales and southern Queensland and is an endangered species in the West owing to hunting and habitat destruction. Everywhere the wilderness habitats of our creatures are shrinking. The eastern quoll has almost certainly been driven from the mainland and is now found only in Tasmania. Similarly, the kowari – also known as the brush-tailed marsupial rat – has found its range becoming increasingly isolated. Once common in the Channel Country, it now digs its burrows only among the sparse vegetation of the Simpson Desert.

The bilby, also known as the rabbit-eared bandicoot or rabbit bandicoot, began to lose ground at the turn of the century. Unique among bandicoots in that it constructs burrows, it ranged freely on the savannah woodlands and shrub grasslands of much of Australia up to eighty years ago. The grazing of rabbits and livestock, together with the introduction of predators, drove out the luckless bilby. It now exists only in the deserts

of Central Australia, with satellite populations in the Kimberly and Warburton regions of Western Australia, because the rich grazing land it once enjoyed has been replaced by hummock grasslands and acacia shrublands. Free surface water is rare in this environment and the bilby must derive most of its water from its food.

Some brightness exists through the gloom created by thoughtless expansion. National parks and reserves preserve the habitats of many species and active work is being done to ensure endangered species are given a new lease of life. Several projects are aimed at protecting species under fire. For example, the New South Wales National Parks and Wildlife Service recently purchased a significant part of the known habitat of the yellow-footed rock wallaby. By protecting a natural domain such as this and by controlling the existence of introduced species or predators, this wallaby wins a second chance.

The single most important factor in reversing the threat to wildlife is man. Our actions or apathy forge the weapons which drive species to extinction yet we flock like the birds we threaten to the wilderness to see the creatures we endanger. More national parks in Australia will ease the pressure and, hopefully, the work underway to restore natural habitats will bring security to the small creatures of the Australian wilderness.

In the world of spiders, such as *Dinopus* species, the males are usually smaller and slimmer than females and thus mating is often a hazardous business for the male. Sperm is transferred in packets, from a special cavity, here seen as a dark disc, at the end of the male's first pair of appendages – known as the pedipalps.

Ground-dwelling brush turkeys
(Alectura lathami) are found in eastern Australia,
north of the Manning River in New South Wales.
The bird pictured was stalking through Lamington
National Park in southern Queensland. Brush
turkeys can fly short distances into trees to
escape predators but they are best known
for the temperature-controlled egg 'incubator'
mounds they construct from leaf litter
on the forest floor.

Millipedes have two pairs of legs
for each body segment. Unlike centipedes, which
are insectivorous, millipedes feed on plant
matter but, like centipedes, they need a certain
amount of moisture or they will rapidly desiccate.

Compared to butterflies, moths are extremely 'downy' – the appearance created by soft scales that cover the moth's body, here extremely exaggerated.

ANT LIONS

Ant lions have two quite different life forms.
As adults they resemble a dragon fly, but it is
as larvae that they earn their name and
fascinating characteristics. The female lays
its eggs in the ground and the larvae, only a few
millimetres long, each build a pit with steep sides.
The larva buries itself in the bottom of the pit
and waits until an unsuspecting ant stumbles
and falls headlong into the trap. If the ant clings
to the walls of the pit, the ant lion larva
uses its body to shower the ant with jets
of sand until the victim loses its footing and
hits the bottom. There the ant lion seizes it in
its pincers, sucks out the body fluid and
throws away the husk.

Butterflies are the adult stage of
one group of insects that undergo complete
metamorphosis from egg to larva to pupa to adult,
the other groups being moths, lacewings, ladybirds,
beetles, ants, flies, mosquitoes and wasps.
Butterflies are characterised by their distinctive
clubbed antennae, here clearly evident in
the skipper butterfly.

Figbirds *(Sphecotheres viridis),* despite
their common name, will also make a meal of
other fruits and berries. These noisy, active birds
chase one another and chatter constantly.

The narrow-nosed planigale *(Planigale tenuirostris)* occurs in inland eastern Australia where it conceals itself in cracks in the soil. Despite the fact that it will eat animals many times larger than itself, it is one of Australia's smallest mammals. The related *P. ingrami* is the smallest.

Short-horned grasshoppers come in
many forms but are all characterised by a cone-
shaped head – sometimes streamlined, sometimes
quite blunt. Short-horned grasshoppers occur
throughout Australia, some on shrubs, some on
grasses, sedges and so on and one species
on the leaf litter of north-eastern
Queensland rainforest floors.

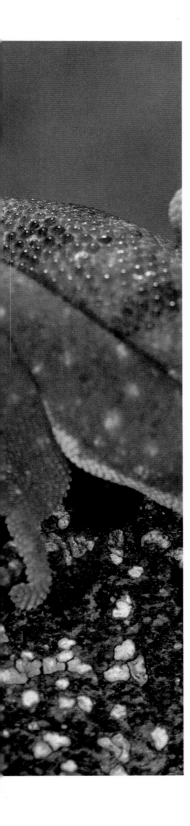

GECKOES

The endearing geckoes have a built-in face washer – their tongues. Unlike many lizards, geckoes do not have moveable eyelids and rely on their tongues to keep their eyes free from grit and dust. More than sixty species of geckoes occur in Australia, most under 10 cm in length, in a variety of habitats. Some are brightly coloured but the majority have dull or mottled skin that merges in with the rocks and bark of their habitats. Some are tree dwellers; others hide during the day under bark or rocks, emerging at night to feed on insects. Many have broad discs on their toes and fingers to make them agile climbers. As well as the novel use of their tongues, geckoes have another interesting adaptation – the ability to shed their tails if they are thereby seized by a predator.

A little black cormorant *(Phalacrocorax sulcirostius)* sits aloof on a rock. The fish-eating cormorants will often work together in a flock to round up a school of fish.

Staring back curiously at the camera,
a common ringtail possum *(Pseudocheirus peregrinus)*
displays its prehensile tail, here hanging
loosely but also used as a fifth limb for climbing
and carrying nesting material.

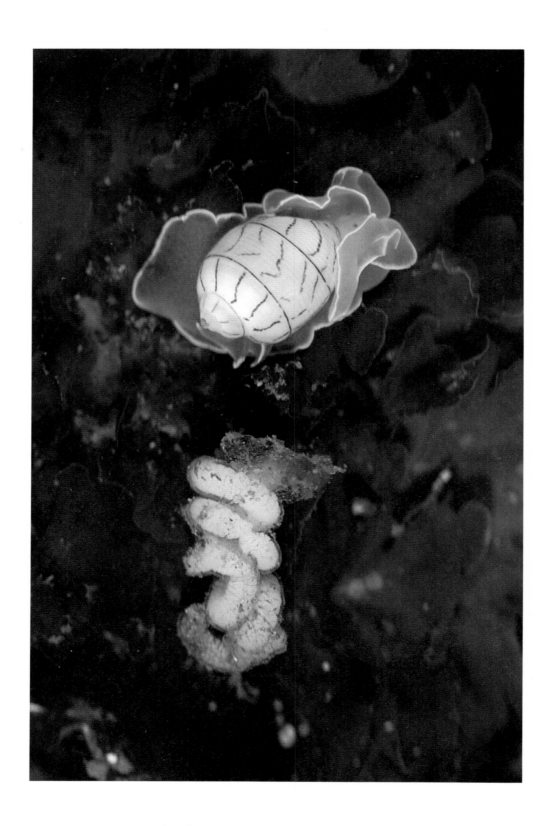

Mollusc eggs are usually laid onto
gelatin-like ribbons stuck to the surface of plants
or rocks. Most often the ribbons form into spirals,
sometimes coloured green or brown. In the case
of the saglossan mollusc *(Oxynoe viridis),* right,
the eggs can be seen as a white ribbon
emerging from the female's body.

Moths are often regarded as nocturnal but many, such as the amatid moth *(Amata trigonophora)*, are common day moths. The amatid feeds on fallen foliage and blooms.

Ladybirds are small beetles, mostly
carnivorous, which control many small pests
of shrubs and flowers. However, the yellow,
twenty-eight spotted ladybird and some others
are leaf eaters and cause damage to crops.
Ladybird larvae of the orange insectivorous type
(*Epilachna* species) resemble mealy bugs,
a clever adaptation to ensnare their look-alike prey.

SHIELD SHRIMP

The arid heartland of Australia seems a strange place to find a shrimp. However, the shield shrimp *(Triops australiensis),* which earns its common name from the large shield covering the front of its body thrives in the dry, baked terrain. Without the rainless periods it would die out, for its lifestyle is geared to irregular rainfall. The minute eggs, often windborn for great distances (some have even been found in Sydney), need a period of desiccation before they can hatch but they also need the rain to develop quickly into adults. Although the maximum adult size is only 4 cm, the Central Australian pools and lakes which form after rain teem with shield shrimps in their tens of thousands.

In ancient Egypt scarab beetles had
religious significance but they are less hallowed
in modern times. The scarab beetle *Diaphonia
dorsalis,* left, is extremely common but, despite
occurring almost everywhere in Australia, surprisingly
little is known about it. Although the colouring
differs, this scarab often is wrongly referred
to as a Christmas beetle.

Tortricid moths are small, primitive
creatures, with no especially appealing features.
However, the larvae of many of the Australian
species are vitally important in their role of
helping to break down leaf mould to form soil
and release plant nutrients.

Female sawflies have a toothed,
saw-like ovipositor which they use to cut slits into
bark for laying eggs. In the species *Perga dorsalis*
and others, the larvae, which resemble the
caterpillars of moths and butterflies, often gather
together when they are not feeding. If disturbed,
they rear their tail ends and tap the branch in
annoyance; further threats cause them to squirt
an odious fluid to deter predators.

Graceful brolgas *(Grus rubicundus)* hover before landing and dance in formation, trumpeting loudly and leaping into the air. Aboriginal legend has it that Buralga was a famous dancer who was transformed into a bird – thus the name brolga.

A shy superb lyrebird *(Menura novaehollandiae)* is poised for escape. Superb lyrebirds are generally regarded as ground-dwelling birds but are best known for their clear, beautiful song (as well as superb mimicry) which can last up to twenty minutes and earns the species the place of top singer out of all the world's birds. In the mating display the male spreads its tail in a spectacular fan. Two species of lyrebird exist and occur in small pockets of rainforest in eastern Australia.

AUSTRALIA'S leading wildlife photographer, Leo Meier, spent more than three years stalking the small creatures of the Australian Wilderness.

"You can squat for hours outside a shy insect's home. You know he's in and he senses you're 'out there'. You just have to wait for the moment when his curiosity gets the better of him."

"I waded through mangroves, slithered through rainforests and climbed rock walls and trees that should have died of old age last century. I was dirty, wet, cold, hot… sometimes all at the same time. But the unique beauty of the Australian wilderness and its fascinating creatures made it hard to come back to the city."

All photographs in this book were taken with Nikon cameras on Kodachrome 25 and 64 films.